BLOOMING PREGNANT!

The Real Facts About Having a Baby...

Foreword &. text by
Cathy Hopkins

Introduction & Memoirs of a mum-to-be
by
Kay Burley

Cartoons by
Alison Everitt

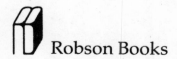 Robson Books

First published in Great Britain in 1993 by Robson Books Ltd,
Bolsover House, 5–6 Clipstone Street, London W1P 7EB

British Library Cataloguing in Publication Data
A catalogue record for this title is available from the British Library

ISBN 0 86051 877 9

Phototypeset by Intype, London
Printed and bound in Great Britain by
Butler & Tanner Ltd, Frome and London

CONTENTS

Other books by Cathy Hopkins are:

Girlchasing: How to Improve Your Game
Manhunting: A Girl's Guide to the Game
69 Things to do When You're Not Doing It:
    the in-Between Lovers' Handbook
The Joy of Aromatherapy
Keeping It Up: How to Make Your Love Affair
    Last Forever
Revenge of the Essex Girls

Other books by cartoonist and TV presenter
    Alison Everitt are:

The Condom Book for Girls
That's Fashion!
The Modern Girl's Book of Torture: A Realistic Look
    at Health and Beauty
Revenge of the Essex Girls
A User's Guide to Men

ACKNOWLEDGEMENTS

WITH SPECIAL THANKS TO:
Val Acar, Judy Bould, Margaret Brannan, Greta and Steve
Brenman, Sali Brookes, Annabel Cheetham, Libby Chilton,
Liz Dunnell, Anna Fairfax Jones, Rosie Ford, Ildi Gerrard-
Banister, Pippa Jackson, Marian and Richard Jeffrey, Theresa
McFarlane, Jane McNeil, Mary O'Leary, Lesley Singleton, Mrs
Clarice Waddington, Nicki Walker and Charlotte Wolffe.

And especially, thanks to Mr and Mrs Hopkins and Mr and
Mrs Everitt for all they must have gone through with children
like Cathy and Alison.

And finally to Steve Kutner for making Kay suffer nine
months of hell, all in the name of love.

FOREWORD

You've seen the movie.

'OK, Hoss, git the hot water and the towels. Maw's havin' the baby.'

A bit of squawking in the distance and it's a convenient CUT TO: Maw sitting up in bed looking radiantly happy holding a beatific sleeping baby as the proud father puffs his cigar and struts like John Wayne, saying proudly, 'That's ma boy.'

Really? That easy, huh? Not according to what I've seen, heard and read lately. More like 'Maw' is half dead with exhaustion, her husband's still under the bed where he hid with embarrassment during the 'transition', when she announced to him and the rest of the hospital staff that he'd never satisfied her sexually . . . *ever* . . . and the beatific babe? – bright blue with spots and a pointy head. *That's* my boy?

And what happens in between? It can be sublime, it can be ridiculous. The only certain factor is that, from conception to the birth, it's different for everyone.

If you're unsure about where you fit in, as your feelings and attitudes don't match those in the 'how to be a perfect mother' books – read on, any unspoken conspiracy to keep mum about becoming a mum is about to be broken! And you can be sure when you've finished reading that you'll know you are in good company in *not* floating through the nine months bathed in a golden glow to emerge as a resplendent madonna at the other.

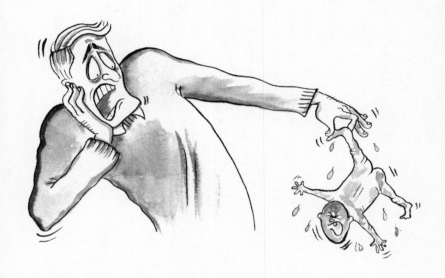

That's my boy??!

INTRODUCTION BY KAY BURLEY

Discovering you're pregnant has to be one of the most confusing times in a woman's life.

I was exhilarated, nauseous, expectant, confused, anxious, proud and every other adjective that comes to mind.

Almost immediately, I had skin like the dark side of the moon, became the size of a small semi before I'd even bought the predictor kit, my feet swelled so much all I could wear was a pair of trainers or tatty black leathers that resembled cast-offs from an overworked traffic warden, and worst of all (my husband would say) I had the temperament of a preying mantis.

It's the longest nine months I have ever known, with the last two weeks, when I was overdue, making it feel like the gestation period of an elephant.

For me, pregnancy was tough. For you it may be different. If, though, you're feeling like you must be the only woman who has ever found pregnancy purgatory then read on.

• First and foremost, I was offered an awful lot of advice while I was pregnant. All of it different and more often than not completely conflicting. So which should I take on board and which should I discard?

• The modern midwife had her views, the health visitor offered her twopence' worth, and the doctors played it by the book.

• Then there was my mother, who after all, she reminded me at almost hourly intervals, did a good enough job when she was carrying me.

• Pregnant friends I found were a pretty good bet. They knew what it was like to struggle through pregnancy (few of them sailed through it). Others, with new babies, were experiencing the new-mum paranoia.

They warned of the sleepless nights, crying for no reason, sore cracked nipples (try grated carrot or cabbage leaves in your bra, they told me, if it doesn't work you can always make it into coleslaw instead) and empathized with the feeling that no one warned you just how bad it can get!

So, the advice I can now offer as a qualified and highly experienced mother of two weeks is take it all in. I didn't discount any of it, some of it I even found useful, but at the end of it I went by my instincts. Me, my body and then, nine months later, my baby are all working it out between us.

Above all, for goodness' sake, hang on to your sense of humour!

1 ONE TOO MANY BABYCHAMS

Let's start at the beginning – at that 'sacred' moment of conception:

THE MYTH

A special night filled with romance and atmosphere. A sky bright with stars. Magic in the air. A candlelit room. He gazes deep into your soul, you return his look, steady, certain. Your hearts beat in perfect time. There's an extra charge in the air. An intangible presence. You both know. You're both ready to bring a new soul into existence. Bit of a misconception if you ask me.

THE REALITY

'We were both drunk as skunks – one too many Babychams.'

'You know the joke. What do you call people who use the rhythm method? Parents. That was us.'

'I forgot to take my pill.'

'I read an article saying that if you'd been on the pill as long as seven years, it would probably take that long to conceive when you come off it. It took three weeks.'

'Laurence was our first. He was a cap-and-two-pessary baby. Jack was born the next year, followed five minutes later by my coil.'

'The condom burst.'

'Wot condom?'

'I got angry with the neighbours and had to take it out on someone so I went to bed with my boyfriend. Was the best sex we ever had. The Jones'll never know that they're responsible for our Henry.'

'Bored at Christmas/New Year/summer holidays . . .'

'There was nothing on the telly.'

'It was winter, the heating broke down, we were cold . . .'

'Me mum never told me that's how you got pregnant!'

'Got the colours mixed up on the "know when you're ovulating" pack.'

'We were celebrating the builders going.'

'Can't remember wot 'appened.'

'A friend of mine confused her valium with her birth control pills – she had fourteen kids but didn't give a shit.' *Joan Rivers*

> Sister Susie built her hopes
> On the book of Marie Stopes.
> But I fear from her condition
> She must have read the wrong edition.

> *Madge Kendall*

And that special, romantic, magical place?

Back of a Ford Cortina.

Over the kitchen table.

The park. An unexpected prick in the rose garden.

Box at the theatre.

Under the desk at work.

Over the ironing board.

On a sheer cliff overlooking a Scottish loch.

On the bathroom floor.

The mile-high club:

Child: 'Mum, we're doing a project for sex education at school. Where was I conceived?'

Mum: 'Er . . . um . . . somewhere between Gatwick and Singapore!'

Child: 'Amazing! Same as the girl that sits in front of me!'

This can all be a bit alarming when you read that Sheila Kitzinger recommends that the conditions surrounding the birth room be as like the 'conception' place as possible! Hospital staff these days are pretty flexible when it comes to bringing in birthing pools but they may draw the line at you wanting to give birth on the back of a Harley-Davidson, out of your brains on Tequila Sunrises because that's where and how you conceived.

And why decide to have a baby in the first place?

The reasons are many and varied:

• You love babies . . . a possibility, but have you ever been left alone with one for 48 hours?

• It's the ultimate experience – to have the child of someone you love . . . What about if you get divorced, end up hating your partner and the child is the spitting image of your ex in looks *and* personality?

• To carry on the family name . . . Pratt, Athol, Donga. Are you sure you want to carry this on? What if your surname's Soul and you want to name her after your grandma, Rachel? R. Soul. Or your great-auntie Annie – A. Pratt, W.C. Orson Cart; Peter Ennis; Anne Tique; Mike Hunt; Tom and Tim, the Bowler twins. The list is endless.

'We call our baby Teeny. We'd call him Martini but he isn't dry enough.' *Anon.*

15

- A child is the only thing that's completely yours alone . . . that is, until puberty, when they disown you and go out glue sniffing.
- To prove your masculinity . . . can be difficult when young Cecil comes out of the closet at sixteen.
- To see the union of your and your partner's genes . . . what if the kid gets all the dud ones and looks like my favourite Martian?
- Someone to look after you in old age . . . kind of difficult if they emigrate to Australia.
- 'My sister was having one!'
- 'I thought if I don't have one soon it'll be too late.'
- To bond your marriage/partnership . . . dream on. The string of sleepless nights and the demands of a young baby put an enormous strain on the best of relationships.
- A let-out from an unhappy job – but the hours are worse, there are no lunch breaks, no tea breaks, and holidays are non-existent.
- Immortality . . . a few months with a sleepless baby and mortality offers sweet escape!

Not that all these reasons can't also be totally valid; of course they can, but don't say you haven't been warned. Every up has a down; every joy, a sorrow; every adorable toothless smile, many nights of teething to come.

TIPS

- So in conclusion and taking note of all that has gone before in this chapter, watch out when you hear the words:

  'Trust me, it'll be all right . . .'

  'I'm bored, what shall *we* do?'

  'You're not getting any younger . . .'

  'I've missed the last train. Can I stay on your couch?'

'Isn't it about time . . . ?'

'I'm on the pill' (and *he's* the one who's saying it. Not that I want to be sexist here but have you ever known a man who knows where his glasses/car keys/house keys are? Never mind his birth pills!)

Memoirs of a mum-to-be

0-1 months

- Where and when did I conceive?

Having only been married six weeks, remembering the time of conception is almost impossible! All I can tell you is that the earth was still rocking wildly at that time.

So to remember where we conceived is inconceivable.

- Why did I want a baby?

The natural-childbirth tomes wax lyrical about how you have your life enriched for ever by a little person whom you can love and cherish and who in return would be totally reliant on you for the next eighteen years . . . Should have read them before I found myself 'up the duff', I suppose – would never have done it!

It has to be said though that my husband is such a wonderfully handsome man that it would have been a complete waste for him to have kept his genes in his jeans.

Desire to carry on the family name? Not on my part, my married name is Kutner – often mistaken for Cunter, and the nervous giggling associated with it; but more of that later.

Like all thirtysomething women, I had often fantasized about a blooming pregnancy. Rocking gently to and fro surrounded by knitting and baby-care books while the sun streamed through the Laura Ashley-trimmed sash window. Followed nine months later with my very own designer baby, perfectly well behaved, beautifully presented and only speaking when spoken to!

And then there's wanting to have a bit of extra time off work perhaps. One friend told me she couldn't wait to get pregnant so she could taken eleven weeks off before and six weeks afterwards while still getting paid – if she'd known what hard work it was carrying the little bugger, delivering it, then feeding every two hours in the middle of the night while trying to continue functioning as a human being, I'm sure she'd have thought seriously about having a goldfish instead!

So why did I decide to become pregnant? After much analysis and soul searching, I've concluded it was probably because I forgot to take my pill!

2 TWO'S COMPANY

'Dear Mary, We all knew you had it in you.'
Dorothy Parker

THE MYTH

She: 'Darling I have something to tell you.'
He: 'What's that, darling?'
She: 'I'm pregnant, darling!'
He: 'Darling, darling that's *won*derful . . .'
Kiss, clinch, fade out . . .

THE REALITY

'Whose is it?' (husband)

'Are you sure it's mine?'

'Are you sure it's *yours*?'

'If *you're* going to have a new baby, I'm gonna have a new car!'

'Oh hell, NO! I'm too young to be a grandma' (40-year-old mother)

'You've got to be joking' (eight-year-old son)

'You've got to be joking' (38-year-old husband)

'You've got to be joking' (68-year-old father)

'Damn it! We've only been married five minutes.'

'I'm not getting rid of the dog.'

'Nowt to do with me, I was on holiday' (husband)

'I don't care as long as it doesn't get put in *my* bedroom. Everyone's always putting stuff in my room! (ten-year-old boy)

'Giddle Goddle!' (Scottish for Good *God!*)

'How will *you* manage?'

'You're not the type.'

'Rather you than me, matey.'

'So what?'

'Can't we have a poodle instead?' (three-year-old)

'About bloody time!'

'But we can't afford it.'

'Oh dear. . .'

'I don't want to talk about it. . .'

'Eee'eck, I can't see *you* with a baby.'

A lot of women said they felt coy telling their parents as although they'd been married for years, they were admitting they'd had SEX!

It's also a time of tremendous adjustment, especially if a woman has been independent, with a career, and suddenly finds herself dependent on her partner, she may find the altered balance of the relationship difficult to accept.

TIPS

- If you don't get the reaction and support you want and need from where you expect it, find it elsewhere with a friend or from the National Childbirth Trust (NCT) who have their headquarters at Alexandra House, Oldham Terrace, London W3 6NH, tel. 081–992 8637.

- As with all major changes in life, it's *so* important to keep talking to each other at every stage. Fears, hopes, what he expects, what she expects. Money – who's going to earn it? What adjustments have to be made? Who'll look after baby during the night, in the evening? Roles? Baby care? Housework? Look for the seeds of problems before they grow and get it *very* clear early on so that assumptions don't set in, to be followed swiftly by resentment.

- Some women prefer to limit the number of people told until the first three months are safely past (as these can be the months that carry the most risk of anything going wrong). If you're feeling queasy but don't want to let on that you're pregnant and don't want to tell lies, try saying, 'I think I'm sickening for something' – which in a sense is true!

- As far as public reaction to pregnancy goes – chivalry is dead, plus it's a cruel trick of nature that early on in pregnancy (when it doesn't yet show) is usually the time you feel the worst. If people don't let you sit down on the tube/bus, my friend Theresa suggested this subtle tactic: Try saying, 'I'm pregnant. If you don't let me sit down, I'm going to be sick all over you.'

★ ★
What was your first reaction on discovering that you were pregnant?

- 'Aaaargh! ! !'
Sue Dawson (Gill in *EastEnders*)
- 'Delight'
Jeffrey Archer
- 'About time! (I'd been married three months)'
Maureen Lipman
- 'Shock horror'
Gray Jolliffe (cartoonist and creator of 'Wicked Willie')
- 'Oh *no*! The predictor *must* be faulty!'
Kay Burley

21

And what was your partner's reaction?

- 'Arrrgh! !'

Sue Dawson

- 'Wondered if she could have the child after her students had completed their exams. I explained nine months was the rule whether she liked it or not.'

Jeffrey Archer

- a) 'Thank God.' b) *'Now* will she be happy?' c) 'Where will it sleep?'

Maureen Lipman

- 'Great! Will he play for Arsenal or have a forehand like Agassi?'

Steve Kutner (Kay's husband)

Memoirs of a mum-to-be
1-3 months

Oh my God, I think I'm pregnant!

There are many ways you can tell when you're pregnant, they told me. A wonderful warm glow inside perhaps, or the need to rest a little more after a hard day at work – not me.

- The realization

I was on holiday on the beautiful isle of Madeira with my new husband. The sun shone incessantly, the warm crystal-clear sea lapped lazily against the shore, the hotel pool was the temperature of perfectly controlled bath water and waiters were on hand to cater for your every whim. I meanwhile had my head stuck down the craftsmen-carved toilet bowl.

My suspicions were obviously alerted then, but I decided a Portuguese predictor kit may not be all that reliable and anyway I was sure I just couldn't be.

Returning home though, the odds narrowed even further when I found myself crying rather than laughing at the script of *Eldorado*. Then, when less than a month after my last period, I could no longer zip up any of my clothes, there seemed little need for a predictor pack.

I bought one anyway – can you believe the price of them? – and yep there it was, two blue lines signalling nine further months of pre-baby blues.

- You're going to be a daddy

I rang Steve at the office and, as Cathy says, he was ecstatic. Like in the best Hollywood movies I thought he'd say, 'Darling that's wonderful, he'll look just like you, let's go for a romantic dinner tonight to celebrate.'

Instead, he said, 'Brilliant, I'm in a meeting though, I'll have to call you back . . . and oh, by the way, Happy Snappy (our family crocodile) is staying.' Steve didn't mention the geckos, chameleon, iguana and snakes, but I anticipated they'd also be nestling down with my newborn. (When he'd said he had a passion for wild animals, I thought he meant me . . . until I went back to his flat!)

My pregnancy hormones were already wavering on the edge of uncontrollable but I managed a fingernail grip on self-control, safe in the knowledge he'd be home that night clutching a bottle of champagne and attempting not to trip over a teddy bear the size of King Kong.

Well, it was a four-pack of Guinness, good for me and the baby apparently, and a baby-gro with 'I dribble better than

Arsenal' emblazoned across it!

- As for Grandma

My mother was delighted and wanted to catch the next train down from Lancashire – still not sure why.

Warning her not to mention it to anyone until after I had passed the three-month watershed was like warning Prince Charles about the dangers of using a mobile phone. She just couldn't control herself and in true northern fashion had told the whole street before I'd even replaced the receiver.

- Then there's telling the other side

My mother-in-law flew in from New York and insisted on carrying my purse and my shopping, and that I rest as much as possible – even though I was still less than ten weeks pregnant!

Of course I would have him circumcised and what about Gideon as a name. I didn't endear myself by saying Gid the Yid would be a dreadful nickname at school. Anyway, what if it's a girl? – don't be silly, it's bound to be a boy, Steve would only father a boy first. (What did she mean first? – there aren't going to be any more, I thought, but bit my lip.) There and then I decided on Alexander for a boy, Grace for a girl.

- At the office

'Oh my God,' they said, 'not *another* one. Must be something in the coffee.' I was the 23rd expectant mum at Sky Television so far that year!

- Animal instincts

My puppy Fred Setter had mixed feelings, but he put aside selfish toddler-type thoughts of having to share his mum's affection with another baby in the family and has been my constant companion, confidant and soggy paw to weep on ever since – what a guy.

25

3 BLOOMING PREGNANT

THE MYTH

You look and feel fabulous.

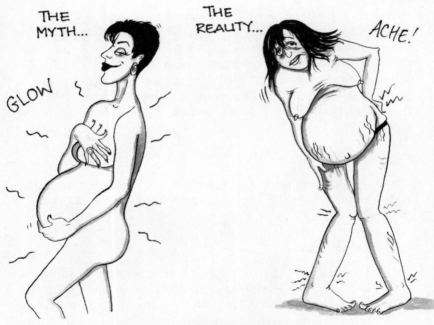

It's all so natural, you'll intuitively know what to do.

You know the minute you're pregnant.

26

THE REALITY

Doctor: What do you want first, the good news or the bad?

Patient: The good.

Doctor: The good news is that you're pregnant, the bad – it was due last Tuesday.

And as for feeling fabulous, here are a few of the symptoms that you might have at some stage of your pregnancy:

Swollen, sometimes painful breasts.

Mood swings/emotional schizophrenia.

THE MYTH....

THE REALITY....

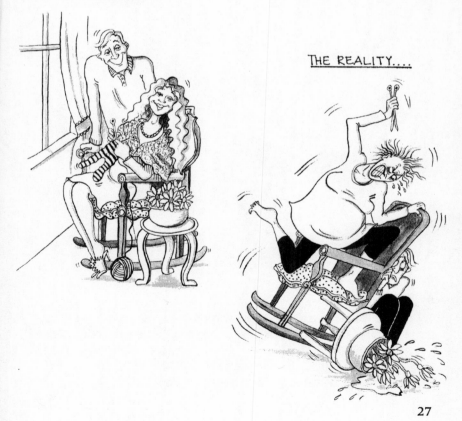

Morning sickness. Although why it was ever called so beats me. From what I can make out you're *lucky* if it only lasts the morning. It ought to be called Martini sickness. Any time, any place, anywhere. Middle of the night, in the afternoon. On the bus, in the supermarket, on an important evening out with your partner's boss. It has no scruples, preferences or guarantees. My friend Marian felt sick on the way to an important meeting, she rushed to the nearest public bin, pushing people over in her panic. She got there just in time to be sick but as she looked down saw it was one of those litter bins that are criss-cross wire at the bottom and it had gone all over her shoes and stockings.

Fatigue.

You may find there are also things you can no longer go near, certain smells – perfumes, onions or garlic cooking – cigarettes, alcohol, coffee . . . your partner. Don't worry. It will pass – though those women who reported going off their husbands said wistfully, 'Give yourself time.'

A tinny taste in the mouth.

Feeling away with the fairies/stupid/up in the air.

Needing to pee a lot – a killer if you're out and can't find a loo, and although pregnant women and young children are permitted to pee on the street, squatting down in Sloane Street might not be quite your style. Someone told me of a law she'd heard about dating from the seventeenth century that says if a pregnant woman out in public needs to 'go', she may approach a policeman and ask him to spread his cape so she can pee in privacy behind him. Trouble is, today it seems to be only mounted police who wear capes and then only in the cold or wet weather. Either way the horse might not be too happy about it!

Leg cramps.

Piles.

Varicose veins.

Heartburn.

Swollen ankles.

Weight gain and a half. (At one time women were told what the 'correct gain' was – not more than 28 pounds over the whole pregnancy. Although excessive weight gain can cause problems, these days it's pretty well recognized that everyone's different.)

Loss of space. You have quite possibly spent months, even years, establishing a healthy relationship where you and your partner give each other space. Time alone. And now this creature, not having read *Cosmopolitan*'s latest article on the subject, is invading not only your home and your life but also your *body*. And then of course, there's the whacky cravings. Here are just a few that have been mentioned: Strawberries and pickles, ice cream and gherkins, pumpernickel, bananas, curry and chips, marmalade and sausages wrapped up in jelly, ginger, beer, steak and kidney pie, peppers, Chinese food, disinfectant, sand, mothballs, chalk, silver polish, toothpaste, earth, charcoal, detergent, soap, pet food, limescale out of the kettle (mmm yum), wax, paraffin and coal! (The latter are possibly an indication of deficiency in iron or other minerals.)

One woman said her cravings would come in the middle of the night and so she used to take a whole load of food to bed with her and line it up alongside the bed. The romance of champagne and oysters replaced by the necessity of pickled gherkins and cocktail sausages.

And this is only the start of that blissful state of mother-to-be-dom.

★ ★

What were the best moments of the whole pregnancy?

- 'The conception'
  Rory McGrath
- 'Seeing Mary fat for the first time'
  Jeffrey Archer
- 'Meeting other emu-shaped women at breathing class'
  Maureen Lipman

- 'Holding Joe in my arms for the first time – love at first sight'
  Sue Dawson
- 'Seeing Alexander wave to his parents via the ultrasound scan'
  Kay Burley
- 'Discovering we were going to have a boy: women's tennis is crap'
  Steve Kutner

And what were the worst moments?

- 'Hormonally screwed up. Weight gain. Everything not being right in my head'
  Helen Lederer
  - 'Being woken several times in the night'
    Jeffrey Archer
  - 'Migraine constantly for three months'
    Maureen Lipman
    - 'The whole pregnancy'
      Mary McGrath
- 'Arsenal losing to Spurs in the 1991 FA cup semi-final'
  Rory McGrath
    - 'Missing Arsenal play'
      Steve Kutner
- 'Nausea, heartburn, indigestion, varicose veins, swollen legs and ankles, nearly three stone of excess weight . . . need I go on . . .'
  Kay Burley
    - 'The nine months'
      Gray Jolliffe

★   ★

'You know more than you think you do' *Dr Spock*

These days so much is written about having a baby. It's confusing enough with all the hormones going haywire without having to contend with so many experts and each

31

with a different opinion to give as to what's best for the birth: to have the baby at home or in hospital, in private or with the NHS, 'natural' or drugged to the hilt, on land, under water, squatting . . . or in the ocean with the dolphins?

Not like the old days when you got the local midwife in and your only pain relief was a towel tied to the bedpost for you to pull on when the pain got bad. And at the turn of the century some women hadn't a clue not only how the baby came out, but how it had got in there in the first place! These days, with NCT and other antenatal classes and endless books and baby experts only too happy to give their opinion on how it should be done, a woman can be well informed if not a little weighed down with facts and information throughout her pregnancy.

There are pros and cons to all of it. It's marvellous that in this day and age there are plenty of options, so best to read up as much as possible in order to make an informed choice. Try not to be swayed by the inevitable pressure from some of your friends and neighbours who insist that their way is best. Different strokes for different folks – let it all sink in and give yourself time to find out what appeals to you. And remember you can always change your mind.

One of the major decisions to be made early on in pregnancy is do you want a home or a hospital birth? Suddenly what should be a simple decision becomes loaded as both factions bear down with 'horror' stories in order to pull you into their camp:

'We can't take responsibility if you do it at home.'

'We know of some *disas*trous home births.'

Thus the hospital lobby, while on the other hand:

'Go into hospital and they give out epidurals without thinking.'

'They fill you full of drugs you don't need which affect the baby.'

Not all of it is necessarily true or applies to everyone, but the advice and tales of woe continue. And what happens? Fear.

Not a resolution. Fear. And that's exactly what you don't want. For a new mother, it's a journey into the unknown – what people fear most – the unfamiliar, where we may have no control. And what can you do with all those sincere souls eager to enlighten you with the correct way to give birth?

Listen to both points of view, decide what feels best for you, then get on with it and try to put any negative thoughts aside. Thousands of babies are born every day, at home and in hospital. Check your facts, make your decision, have a cup of tea and get on. Chances are you'll be fine.

The 'domino' (Domiciliary-In-Out) scheme, if it works in your area, seems to combine the best of what both home and hospital have to offer: you have the same midwife throughout your pregnancy, she goes into the hospital with you, stays through the birth, goes home with you and sees to your aftercare.

★ ★

Would you advise a home or a hospital birth?

- 'Hospital'
Maureen Lipman
- 'Hospital or someone else's home'
Rory McGrath
- 'Home if possible'
Sue Dawson
- 'Either, as long as it's not in the ambulance between the two!'
Kay Burley

★ ★

TIPS

- Skip the first three months, start on the fourth!

- Don't feel guilty if you're not floating through it wrapped in a golden glow of inner contentment. Guilt is a wasted emotion. No matter how you go through your pregnancy, there will be someone somewhere to tell you you'd have had a better experience if *only* you'd done this or not eaten that. Read the books, listen to the advice then do what feels right for you.

- Take something to do while you're waiting to see the doctor on your visits to the clinic.

- If you're throwing up a lot, carry some sort of plastic carrier bags (preferably not see-through!) so you're not caught out ... (and don't forget something to fasten it with ... sellotape or a rubber band).

- You don't need to eat for two but let's face it, when else can you get away with it?

- Eat bread or dry crackers to stave off morning sickness.

- Heartburn can apparently be helped by sleeping with the shoulders propped up . . .

- Leg cramps by the legs propped up. God help you if you've got both!

- Ask your partner to take on more household chores: he can't carry the baby – yet – but he can help in other areas.

- Tell people what you want for the baby, otherwise (the wedding and toaster syndrome) you end up with 40 pairs of small bootees.

- On visits to the clinic, write down all your questions before-hand, as if there are a lot of people waiting you may feel pressurized to hurry, and forget what you wanted to ask. How are you supposed to know, if it's your first child? It's a bit like going to the hairdresser's – you have to know what you want before you go in, and be prepared to be assertive.

Questions you may like to ask

Will I be shaved?

Will I be given an enema? (Most hospitals don't do either any more but no harm in checking!)

What's the hospital's policy if the baby is overdue?

What pain relief will be made available to me and what effect will it have on me and the baby?

What tests will I be given and why?

Will I be able to move around during labour?

Can my partner/friend stay with me throughout? Even if I have to have a Caesarian?

Can the baby stay with me afterwards?

Will the baby be delivered straight on to my breast?

Do I want this?

Do the staff put a time limit on any of the stages of labour?

How long are the doctor's and midwive's shifts?

He's showing positive signs of becoming an accountant... but don't let it worry you....

- Talk to other women who've had babies and ask them to help you work out your list of questions.

  If the hospital won't answer any of these questions, find out through the NCT from women who have given birth in the same place.

- If you don't understand anything, ask. One lady was told she had a retroverted uterus as if she was supposed to know what it meant. She sat there demurely, inwardly making her will and thinking 'Oh my God I'm gonna die, I got a retroverted uterus.' Don't be fobbed off by 'You don't need to worry.'

- Ultrasound tests aren't always right in determining the sex of the baby. It has been known for staff to say it's a boy – they saw a willie – so you decorate the nursery blue, your husband buys his season ticket for the football and, lo and behold, it's a girl. I'm surprised the *Sport* hasn't picked up on this one. 'SHOCK! HORROR! BABY HAS SEX CHANGE IN THE WOMB' with pictures from the scan alongside pictures of the newborn. 'The astonishing strength and sheer willpower of the unborn! Read all about it!'

- Make informed decisions and try and stay positive. As in all of life, it's not the events alone that determine your experience but how you respond and react to those events. Some women see pregnancy as a major life experience and go into it and all its ups and downs with enthusiasm, others see it as a trial and a burden to be endured and feared. To an extent, you can't control what kind of pregnancy you have. You can have the most optimistic attitude in the world and still have a difficult time, but you can control how you *react* to the situation. How you can make things better for yourself, that choice is yours, especially these days.

Memoirs of a mum-to-be

3-4 months

Blooming pregnant – you have got to be joking.

A blooming mum-to-be at my yoga class said she enjoyed being pregnant so much, she never wanted it to end. Our lovely teacher Yvonne said that that could cause a few problems in wanting to 'release' the baby in labour and as a result the birth may be very slow.

I remember thinking at the time (while attempting to relax totally as shown by Yvonne) that if that was the criterion for a fast or slow birth, my baby would shoot down the birth canal so fast, the doctors would need to be fully kitted up with a baseball glove to catch him.

'How do you feel?' The most often asked question in the early months. In my experience, only tell the questioner if you're feeling wonderful. No one ever wanted to know that I was spewing up my guts, had chronic antenatal blues, couldn't fit into any of my clothes and was swinging erratically between homicide and tear tantrums . . . especially if they were pregnant too! After all, you're supposed to be feeling fabulous, look radiant and to have this uncontrollable maternal desire to dribble over matinée jackets as you browse around Mothercare.

And it is true, people told me constantly how well I was looking, how clear my skin seemed and how my eyes shone. I thanked them kindly, leaving them with no idea what the hormones were doing to me on the inside. I was totally nauseous and eating enough food to put Hulk Hogan to shame. I was so knackered that I found it hard work walking to the fridge (always managed it though).

• Food: All the best pregnancy books warned me never to open my mouth to eat unless I was sure it was benefiting the baby. Easily said. Anything healthy like salads, fruit, nuts etc wouldn't stay down. Instead only greasy, fatty things like chips, sausage rolls or fried egg and bacon butties offered sufficient lining on my stomach to stave off the nausea, at least for an hour or so. I piled on a stone in three months. I consoled myself with the knowledge that Paula Yates had added several stone to her svelte frame during her pregnancy and many of my girlfriends had easily tipped the scales at three stone heavier than their pre-pregnancy weight.

The hospital, though, didn't quite see it like that, warning that it was neither good for me nor for the baby to gain too many kilos (I always worked it out in pounds) and advising sagely that the more weight I gained, the more difficult it would be to lose afterwards.

One book, Gordon Bourne's *Pregnancy*, I found an absolute bible, but it was fatally flawed by warning consistently not to gain more than 9 kilos – didn't even bother to work that out in pounds – I was sure I was already tipping the scales at well past that milestone. What do men know anyway?

Well, Steve certainly knew how to make me feel like an extra for the Honey Monster Ad. I was beginning to need clothing that would double as a motorcycle cover, when as we were preparing to go out for supper one evening he said, 'Are you taking all of that bottom with you? Never mind, darlin', I suppose we can both sit on it.'

Venom, tears and the realization on my man's part that he should keep his pert, perfectly-formed mouth shut in future finally resolved that situation.

The continuing nausea meant I carried on eating what I liked to get me through those first few months. Hopefully it will only last until the fourteenth week at the latest, said the midwife, though no one told my baby that, and my sickness lasted until I'd taken my legs out of the stirrups on the delivery table.

Eventually, I just resigned myself to eating whatever helped and decided to worry about losing weight afterwards ... though the odd double portion of apple crumble and cream (with extra cream on the side) wasn't really that necessary I suppose.

Anyway, I lost two stone or so within ten days of having Alexander, though I'm still trying to shed those extra portions of apple crumble!

• Cravings: Food was mine, Jelly Belly jelly beans in particular – probably because they reminded me of what my jelly belly was already looking like. I read that one mum-to-be had cravings for Edinburgh rock and her husband stoically completed a thousand-mile round-trip up the M1 to satisfy her longing. Steve said a bag of chips on the way home from our NCT class showed he loved me just as much!

Tears and tantrums brought forth a magnificently wrapped heart-shaped box containing . . . Jelly Belly jelly beans!

• Turnoffs: I couldn't bear the smell or taste of some things. I went off coffee, tea, milk, some breads, orange juice, Coca-Cola – in fact, all fizzy drinks except champagne and that they told me I couldn't have . . . if mum's tipsy baby's comatosed . . . I was warned; the odd glass is fine in my experience, though the guilt factor always stopped me enjoying it.

• Other problems: My feet did swell. Try raising them higher than your head when you're resting, I was warned.

Heartburn was a nightmare at night. Try keeping your head higher than your feet, it can help ease indigestion, the midwife advised.

Swollen feet and heartburn – I tried a Houdini contortion manual!

• Weight gain – gentle exercise, but nothing too energetic, I was told.

I did manage the odd aerobics class and was advised that swimming is excellent for both me and the unborn. Well, being the size of a beached whale meant I was never comfortable at the pool and even my best attempts at breaststroke felt like I was swimming on top of a beach ball.

Brisk walking would also be excellent, said the doctor. Fred, my puppy, thought that was the best idea and we clocked up more miles on Hampstead Heath than an athlete training for the London Marathon. Didn't help the figure, was good for the wellbeing, though.

Relaxation – I found this really tough, especially with all that extra blood and hormones swilling around. A massage or reflexology was brilliant, but worked out really expensive.

I joined a yoga class especially for pregnant mums. We spent two hours every Tuesday morning getting ourselves in the sort of positions that had probably helped us conceive in the first place.

- Forgetfulness – my brain must have resembled the consistency of mushy peas. Asking the grey matter to perform even the most straightforward of tasks proved almost impossible.

I remember interviewing Foreign Secretary Douglas Hurd during a live interview on Sky and, despite having prepared for an hour for the interview, when it came to thanking him, I couldn't for the life of me remember his name. Not very impressive.

On a smaller scale, everyday chores from shopping lists to remembering where I'd arranged to meet friends for lunch, or even that I'd promised to meet them at all, was becoming more and more of a problem for the mushy mess that passed for a brain.

I tried writing everything down, but couldn't remember where I'd put the piece of paper.

One thing I did remember though was reading in my mother-and-baby magazines how I should be kind to myself and not expect too much.

On reflection I decided against organizing a contract killing on my unreasonable, uncaring partner, I thought I'd probably need the money for Pampers later on!

4 'I WANT MY BODY BACK'

MYTH

That the pregnant shape is only peculiar to women.

That these days you can
get almost anything to
wear in pregnancy.

You'll feel wonderful.

People are friendlier to you.

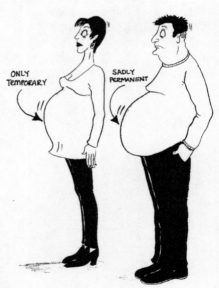

ONLY TEMPORARY

SADLY PERMANENT

THE REALITY

You have days when you feel like a pot-bellied whale.

The public *are* friendlier to you (but not when you vomit on
them).

There may well be a better choice of maternity wear but someone has yet to come up with a pair of tights that don't slip down beneath the bulge.

There are certain films that it is not advisable to see during pregnancy. *Alien* has to be avoided at all costs as you may well be feeling by now that if anything is science fiction, the state of pregnancy surely is. I mean, *another being* is growing inside you and you haven't even been introduced.

There are many advantages to ultrasound scans these days. Should be obvious: you can go along and be reassured by a stranger in a white coat that what is inside you, feeding off you and causing your body to balloon and your emotions to go bonkers, is in fact a baby and not an alien despite what you may be feeling.

Other films not to see include *Rosemary's Baby, The Hand that Rocks the Cradle* and *Fatal Attraction* – when it comes to cinema going, stick to *Bambi,* you'll feel much better.

It's true, remarkable things start happening to the body. It seems to have a mind of its own all of a sudden. Chest size 32A can become 36 triple D. One woman said it was OK at first but she started to get worried when her breasts got bigger than her head; then she used to give people marks out of ten for staring at her three bumps.

My friend Richard told me about a pregnancy class for couples that he'd attended with his wife where a girl sitting at the back of the class put her hand up to ask a question:

'Excuse me, I've been pregnant for two months and I've already put on four stone and it all seems to be around my breasts . . .' Never had he seen so many heads turn so fast, including his.

The way women deal with their ever-expanding situation says a lot about their attitude. Flaunt it or disguise it. And if people say you should be proud of yourself just now, get them one of those mirrors that distorts the image and see how they like it.

There can, though, be a difference between how you see yourself and how your partner sees you.

TIPS FOR PARTNERS

- *What to say*:

Women as always are very quick to spot false flattery. To make false claims – e.g. that she's as slim and lithe as ever when she looks and feels like the Michelin man – can only irritate. Some women feel more feminine when pregnant, but many feel swollen and sexless, and are concerned that their partners won't like them. Reassure her she's still loved. Compliment her on what is true: fabulous skin. Great hair. Ear lobes. 'You *will* get your figure back.' 'I love you.'

- *What not to say*:

'You going out with all that?'

'Gawd, your bottom's ENORMOUS.'

'Ha, ha, ha.'

'Yo, look at the size of those jelubis.'

'Could you walk behind me when we're out?'

'Christ, you're as big as a house.'

'Would you like your food on a tray on your lump?'

TIPS

- Buy styles that suit you – because you're having a baby doesn't mean you have to look like one.

- Swimming is a marvellous relief as it's the only time you can be totally weightless, although one woman reported that after a lovely session in the water, she went to get out and couldn't heave herself up the ladder.

- Have treatments to pamper yourself. Aromatherapy and massage can bring great comfort during this time. Make sure the practitioner is familiar with the oils *not* to be used in pregnancy.

- Don't panic if your weight balloons. My friend Linda put on 4½ stone. She's as thin as a rake now. I only put on two stone – trouble is . . . I'm not pregnant . . .

- Have your hair done, and your toes (you probably won't be able to reach them anyway).

- Do get some exercise: as well as walking and swimming, you can try classes in yoga or other exercises designed specially for pregnant women.

Memoirs of a mum-to-be

4-5 months

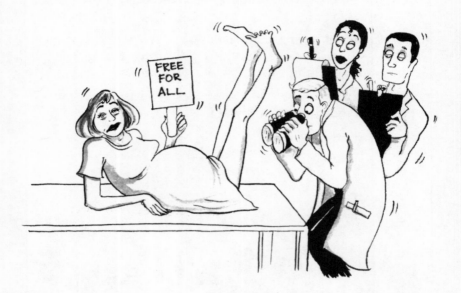

It is time to visit the hospital and from this moment on, even if you haven't felt it before, your body is no longer your own.

I was prodded, poked, had enough blood taken out of me to satisfy Hannibal Lecter, was asked more questions than a Mastermind contestant, and above all was kept waiting long enough to put even British Rail to shame. Welcome to the hospital antenatal visits.

All the NHS staff had my best interests at heart, as well as those of every other pregnant woman there, so they were incredibly overworked. I always had to be prepared to wait at least an hour longer than my appointment time. Is it any wonder my blood pressure was up?

Just as I was dozing off I would hear the lovely Irish nurse call 'Mrs Cunter', which never failed to raise a giggle among the other pregnant mums who had little else to entertain them during the endless wait.

Eventually, I stopped bothering to correct her. We set up a sweep to see if she would mispronounce it every visit – it helped pass the time.

• Tip:

I was always armed with lots of books (pregnancy or baby-care matter was appropriate, but a good Jeffrey Archer was much more interesting). Magazines dating back to the Ark, always with the front cover missing, meant it was better to take my own.

One of our pregnant mums used to carry a copy of *Playboy*. She didn't plan on reading it but it never ceased to raise a few eyebrows – a sense of humour, that's what you need during a two-hour wait.

• Tests:

I'm not qualified to give advice on the tests offered, I can only quote from my experience.

The Triple Marker Test offered me a chance to weigh up the odds of having a Down's Syndrome baby. It was sold to me as a simple blood test, but I don't think I considered it seriously enough and it led to other more invasive procedures.

I had to undergo an amniocentesis, which is usually only offered to women over 37 and involves having a needle inserted through the uterus wall to remove fluid from around the baby. Again it can detect Down's, along with other abnormalities. I found the three-week wait for the results the longest time of the whole pregnancy, in fact the longest 21 days of my life. One plus, we found out 'it' was a he – Alexander it was.

The ultrasound scan was much more fun for all of us. It was like a photo opportunity for Alexander. We could see him paddling away in his amniotic fluid oblivious to an ecstatic mum and dad to be. On the serious side, though, we should have been more aware that it was being done to detect abnormalities.

- Tip:

The medical team told me I should ask them anything I was anxious or curious about throughout my pregnancy. Easy with those who were friendly and approachable, not so those who weren't. I have interviewed politicians, royalty and celebrities around the world, but I still felt completely intimidated by experts in white coats.

I decided to approach hospital visits like a job and wrote down all the questions I wanted answers to, just in case I dried up in the middle. Even better, I took Steve with me to give confidence and moral support. If I completely blew it, he'd take over, and between us we'd cover everything we wanted to know.

The hospital made me very aware of the little alien inside, his needs and expectations, but, I couldn't help thinking, what about *mine*? I was still feeling unloved, unattractive and unwell!

In my heart of hearts I knew that I had a fabulous body; it was just hidden under mounds of excess flesh. 'Fat Mummy' was my latest nickname from the man who I think was beginning to regret having married me in the first place.

I tried to keep on exercising at the gym, but hipporobics was the best I could manage and my inelegant gait meant I was forced to hide at the back of the class.

I began to hate slim women, Demi Moore posing when she was eight months' pregnant made me want to curl up and die; I had a bag of chips instead. I threw away the bathroom scales, wanted to break mirrors and tape up my husband's mouth.

- Buying clothes:

I couldn't fit into anything any more, but I still had a nightly current affairs programme to present so I had no option but to go shopping for clothes. It was a nightmare.

Changing rooms just aren't meant to cater for two of you. One of you with an extra large bum as well. Sales assistants tried to be helpful and nodded knowingly when I said I was searching for something sexy, glamorous and ... er ... shaped like a bin bag.

- Tip:

Black leggings were always my best bet and the baggier the tops the better. Better still, I decided to leave the clothes shopping for nine months and raided Steve's wardrobe instead. Served him right for being so rude all the time.

Some women can still fit into a size 10 at this stage, run two miles before breakfast, have a full day at the office, dash out for supper and still look and feel fabulous. After much deliberation I ruled against sending hate mail or sticking pins into waxwork effigies of them, consoling myself in the knowledge they'd probably be cursed with babies that cried all night anyway!

5 FALLING SHORT OF EXPECTATIONS

THE MYTH

When women are pregnant and become mothers they become the same and automatically get on because of the shared experiences.

THE REALITY

Pregnant women and new mothers are as many and varied as are their partners. No two pregnancies or births are ever the same. All women have in common is the name of their condition.

The mums and mums-to-be

Designer mum – the baby's her latest fashion accessory

New age mum – 'We really wanted an Aquarian baby, with it being the dawning of a new era and all, but at least he'll have his moon in Taurus and that's square to my husband's Sun . . .'

Devoted, liberal mother – treats her lump as a sacred object, will later put her child on a pedestal and be seen in a café in Muswell Hill smiling benignly at her infant as he screams and wrecks the joint and everyone curses her under their breath.

Anyone who dares tell her to discipline her child will be labelled a Victorian childhater.

Martyrs – self-sacrificing, long-suffering. 'No, really,' sigh, 'I can manage,' huff, 'you go and enjoy yourself . . .' sigh, 'I'm used to staying in . . . on my own . . . tired . . . lonely . . .' sigh.

Trojan – 'I'm not *ill*! I'm just *pregnant*.' After the birth she'll go back and finish the letter she was typing when her waters broke.

Perfect mother – having babies is her career. 'Of course I won't *ever* go back to work, or leave my baby to cry or *ever* lose my head . . .' Oh yeah?

The petrified – 'Aaaaagh. I'm gonna die. Ohmagod! I'm having a BABY! . . . The hole's not big enough for it to get out of.'

The reluctant – terrified she's going to end up like her mother so she doesn't do anything until the birth is imminent, then she sends her partner out to Mothercare with a list and a fiver.

The neurotic – obsessively safety-conscious. She'll sterilize everything and won't even take a paracetamol if she needs one – which is often.

The ignorant/innocent – 'Yoh, a baby! Where did that come from?'

By-the-book mother – sails through it all until something the books didn't mention happens – like terrible wind in labour.

The straight-back-into-her-jeans type – (usually aged eighteen).

The Laura Ashley nightie type – most frightening of all, she's often seen beaming from the pages of the Sunday magazine supplements. She'll be dressed in floaty English-rose dress and straw hat (even though it's December) with the baby wearing a matching straw hat draped in flowers and ivy. 'I just lurve every part of being a mother,' she simpers.

The business mother – she's the one in the labour ward with the portable wordprocessor and the exotic, expensive flowers.

Prissy princess – 'I couldn't *possibly* lift a thing. *You* don't know what it's like!'

Make-do mum – baby sleeps in a drawer just like his ancestors and dresses in hand-me-downs.

I'll-do-it-my-way mum – she'll use homoeopathic remedies for nine months, and insist on it all being natural (and probably end up having every drug on offer).

Matter of fact mother – kids soon learn to fend for themselves.

Spoiler – hasn't a clue how to cope, so offers the children bribes to behave from an early age. Her guilt over this causes her to spoil the kids even more.

Earth mother – broad hips from all the organic homemade bread she bakes. The house is full of alfalfa sprouts and children's paintings stuck on to every empty bit of wall.

The fathers and fathers-to-be

The reluctant – 'He finished his drink with a silent toast to Herod' *Kingsley Amis*.

The boy scout father – he'll pack your bag to be prepared, complete with compass, Swiss Army knife, the right coins for the phone, and thermos flask.

The obsessively interested father – taking notes, the whole process becomes his hobby.

The over-enthusiastic father – records everything on his home video to break the ice at dinner parties later. It'll make a change from the where-we-went-on-our-holidays videos!

New age father – don't visit him in the first few weeks or you're likely to get offered mushrooms on toast with fried placenta.

The accountant husband – good for timing all the contractions precisely.

The know-it-all husband – he'll tell her she's not in labour because it's not like the antenatal teacher described it.

The empathizer – he's the one with his empathy belly on, who joins in with the groaning.

The absent father – 'I don't want to talk about it.'

The rejected father – not allowed to be a part of it all.

The chauvinist – ' 'Ts a woman's role, looking after kids.'

The eager – 'Let me, oh do let me cut the umbilical cord.'

The useless – 'Let me, oh do let me cut the umbilical cord. Oops! Sorry, nurse, didn't realize that was your finger.'

Casanova – once inside the hospital, he'll take a turn for the nurse.

The controlling father – 'Drugs aren't good for the baby so my wife *won't* be having any.'

WE'RE pregnant, so we WON'T be feeding our unborn child toxic rubbish like cakes and donuts. .... We'll have a crispbread and a herbal tea...

CAKE COUNTER

The giggler – can't cope with any of it so giggles his way through, especially at antenatal classes as you roll around and simulate various stages of labour. Actually not a bad way to be!

They do try. One woman's partner was so eager to help and insisted on rubbing her back, unfortunately as he leaned over her, he put his out, and as they took her into delivery in a wheelchair, they took him in another wheelchair to another part of the hospital.

- *For the fathers-to-be:* educate yourself. Many men don't know how to support a woman through pain – they just want to *stop* it. They're brought up to 'fix' things. Some men find the experience of watching someone they love in pain unbearable as they are helpless to do anything. This can disturb some women as they become aware of their partner

61

there quietly freaking out. Talk it all through before, or have someone else (mother/friend) there with whom she feels totally comfy.

TIPS

- Be yourself. It's your pregnancy, you don't have to conform to someone else's idea of how it should all be done ... unless of course they offer to babysit when the baby's born, in which case pretend to go along with them.

- Don't leave your urine sample lying around. One woman took hers to the hospital and left it in an open bag in the lobby; when she went to get it for the doctor, it had gone. She'd used a whisky bottle to put it in.

- Don't insist that your partner should be there because it's what's done these days, especially if one of you is not comfortable about it.

- Keep your sense of humour. Hospital visits or classes needn't be horribly serious. Pregnancy and even labour can have their funny side.

Memoirs of a mum-to-be

5-6 months

No getting away from it, I was definitely pregnant.

Up till now I'd more or less managed to get on with my life. As long as there was a cake shop and a loo somewhere in the vicinity, I could cope. Not any more.

Alexander had decided it was much more fun being an active rather than a passive baby-to-be and regularly used my bladder to practise his five-a-side football techniques.

We wanted to go on holiday but as a precaution I was wasn't allowed to fly. It's no fun having a baby at 35,000 feet, the doctor warned, and anyway no one wanted to insure me. So while Steve jetted off to New York (work, of course!) I was left at home to contemplate just how much my life, not to mention my body, was changing. I mused over how I would deal with the rest of my pregnancy. I had hoped I'd be able to sail through it, taking a couple of days off work for the labour and confinement perhaps, then be back in the studio probably within a couple of weeks . . .

Well, perhaps not quite, but I did want to be a modern professional mother and deal with the whole thing in an intelligent rational manner. Instead, I was a weepy, insular, knackered wreck. Even turning over in bed was becoming an effort. Pillows under my knee to give more room for the ever-growing bump helped, but treading a well-worn path to the bathroom at least half a dozen times a night made sleep a much sought-after commodity.

By now those around me were getting a bit bored with my bump too and their comments varied from 'This pregnancy seems to be lasting for ever' – as if I needed to be told that – to 'My God, you look enormous' or 'It seems strange you're so tired. My wife was jogging two miles a day until she was eight months' pregnant.'

I did feel like I was falling short of expectations. The books (Steve complained I was always reading and quoting experts at him) said I should be blossoming into prospective mother-hood by now. The girl at work who was as pregnant as I was still looked like a Roman goddess, and girls at my yoga class were waxing lyrical about just how fabulous it was having this new life forming inside of them and liked nothing better than looking inwards and focusing on their foetuses – YUK!

Thank goodness I still had a few sane humans around who, when I asked how they felt about babies, would say, 'Well, they're all right, but I couldn't eat a whole one. Still, I believe they freeze quite well.'

That's what you need when you're pregnant, at least some less intense friends, with a good sense of humour.

Looking back, I certainly wasn't your earth mother-to-be and I didn't have the energy or the mental stability to be a professional mater. I was probably just a common or garden thirtysomething, attempting to live up to others' expectations and finally accepting the limitations of my mind, body and baby. It's the only way.

And if it all just got too much, there was always my mum. Funny how she always knew just what to say. Hope I will too now I'm a mum!

THE NINE MONTH CALENDAR

THE NINE MONTH CALENDAR

6 WHAT MOMMA NEVER TOLD YOU

'Many women still believe that if they want a male child, the husband should wear his boots at the time of conception'   *Anon.*

THE MYTHS

That friends, relations, even childbirth books tell you the truth about pregnancy, labour and childbirth. For example, here is a random selection of some of the advice given:

Eat cherry pie for a girl, apple pie for a boy.

Eat acid foods for boys, alkali for girls.

Eating shrimps causes babies to have crooked backs. Strawberries cause birthmarks.

Eat fish for a boy; have sex more often if you want a girl.

Douche with cider vinegar for a boy, yoghurt for a girl (prior to conception that is!)

If you dream of skulls, it's a girl; feathers, it's a boy.

If it lies high in the belly, a girl; low in the belly, a boy . . . And vice-versa.

That pregnant women don't want sex.

If your complexion's bad during pregnancy, it's a girl and she's robbing your beauty.

You forget the pain of labour in a few hours.

Giving birth can be like the most intense orgasm you've ever had – !! (It's statements like this that put some people's sexual pleasures into question!)

If the baby is late try: feathers under the nose, sniffing tobacco (actually this isn't as daft as it sounds as sneezing causes the diaphragm to press on the uterus); or castor oil or raw eggs to cause wretching.

That the birth is over when the baby is born.

That all your friends and family will rally round to help afterwards.

And this is just a random selection: advice given to mothers-to-be can be varied and colourful!

THE REALITY

Best way to tell if it's a boy or a girl is forget all the stuff above about shape, dreams and so on – just have a look when it comes out.

Women often do want sex when they're pregnant; in fact some claim to enjoy it more as there is no risk of them getting pregnant! Plus for some women all that pelvic congestion can put them in a permanent state of arousal. As one lady put it, her line was 'Forget the foreplay, just get on with it!'

Giving birth can hurt like hell and no one prepares you for it.

With all that pushing when giving birth sometimes you do a poo. This happened unexpectedly to one woman whose husband had abandoned her some months earlier. Her best friend was present at the birth and as the woman in labour pushed down, instead of a baby appearing, a small neat turd did instead.

Friend: 'Don't worry. It's just a little shit.'
Woman giving birth: 'Takes after its father then, who's a big shit!'

After the baby is born, the placenta is delivered. No one had told my friend Jean this fact, and, after all the straining and pushing she'd done, she thought she'd pushed her liver out after the baby.

You need a lot of help afterwards but, sadly, in our culture the ways of the extended family have now gone. You're on your own.

Your husband will probably dine out on stories of how awful it's all been while you're stuck at home.

TIPS

- Don't believe everything you hear.

- You or your partner may not feel like making love in which case find other ways to express your affection.

RIGHT   WRONG!

★ ★

What advice would you give to a pregnant woman?

- 'Rest and look after yourself because you won't get another chance till they've left home'
  Sue Dawson
- 'Try and skip this part of motherhood ... if not possible, then ignore all advice'
  Kay Burley
- 'Enjoy the peace and rest. It will never be the same!'
  Helen Lederer
- 'Don't always expect to glow. Demi Moore we all ain't!'
  Maureen Lipman
- 'Don't believe anything anyone says, including me'
  Rory McGrath
- 'Don't count the days. And don't call her fat'
  Steve Kutner
- 'Don't get pregnant'
  Gray Jolliffe

★ ★

Memoirs of a mum-to-be

6-7 months

Mum didn't have the answer to everything though, or perhaps she did but was just doing what mums do and protecting me from what lay ahead!

No such qualms from others around me. As I became more and more pregnant and as a result waddled slower and slower, so I found myself weighed down even further by more and more unsolicited advice.

Everyone's an expert on everything from knowing what sex the baby is to how much pain I'd have to suffer during labour and the birth.

Complete strangers would feel it was not in the least anti-social, not to mention downright rude, to rest their clammy little paws on my bump then pronounce confidently that I was definitely having a girl. Others would say 'That bump's low: it must be a boy.' Those who decided to take their life in their hands would even say you've got such a big bottom, it must be a girl!

In my endless quest for knowledge we started our NCT classes, couples course, of course. Unfortunately the first session coincided with Arsenal playing a cup game so I had to go on my own. As we all wriggled nervously in our teacher's living room I found myself saying, 'Sorry my partner's not here, he's at a board meeting,' when in fact he was standing on the terraces cheering on the Gunners!

The week after, I wished there'd been another game when Steve insisted on laughing loudly all the way through our pretend contractions. I wanted to murder him, same emotion in fact as when I was suffering the real thing three months later.

The classes are supposed to prepare you for the birth. Let me assure you nothing, but nothing, prepares you for the birth. My friends tried to warn me, my mother tried to protect me, Steve tried to reassure me, but it was my brain that I had most to thank for miraculously erasing my memory banks the moment my son was born . . . though I did keep wondering how all those stitches had got there!

7 PREPARING FOR THE HAPPY EVENT

'Those wretched babies don't come out until they are
ready' *Queen Elizabeth II*

THE MYTH

Babies come after nine months.

THE REALITY

Babies come when:
You've just sold your house and everything's in packing
cases.

Your husband's just lost his job.

Your husband's abroad on business, the babysitter's
unavailable and you've got three other kids who can't be
left alone.

Your car's broken down and all the taxis are on strike.

The midwife you particularly wanted there is on another
case.

It's a bank holiday and most of the staff are off.

Those relatives you haven't seen for years have arrived from
New Zealand and are camped out on every bit of your

floor space.

There's a major sporting event that *he who usually gets his own way* doesn't want to be dragged away from.

How to recognize that the birth is imminent according to the books

A rush of energy.

Sudden lethargy.

An urge to eat a lot.

Loss of appetite.

A need to go to the loo a lot.

Constipation.

Uhm. Well that makes it all *very* clear; now we know *exactly* what we're looking for! (Besides which, *all* of those symptoms might occur at any time from day one of the pregnancy.)

The last few weeks can be the most difficult, there you are – your birthing pool and Janet Balaskas's book on active birth packed along with your secret supply of opium. And it's the waiting game.

Depending on whether it's going to be a home or hospital birth, there are certain objects and items some of the girls I spoke to said you might like to have along in your labour-room bag:

Socks.

Nice spray smells as you may . . . expel air (i.e. fart).

Evian spray (for squirting at whoever you feel like).

Food – light and easy to digest (although some hospitals won't let you eat at all in case you need an anaesthetic); something to drink – maybe fruit juice or cool water.

A fan (not the cheerleader variety although a team of them may help as well, rather a fan to keep you cool).

Music.

Reading matter, paper and pen, games – anything to while away the hours.

Something to make a hot compress for the small of your back.

A mirror (for her to watch the head come out, not for him to admire himself).

Oil for massage.

Aromatherapy oils (some of the oils can really help in labour – ask a local practitioner to make up a blend for you).

Paper bag for hyperventilation (you put it over your nose and mouth if you hyperventilate – it'll force you to breathe more slowly).

Some natural remedies to help – Rescue Remedy (one of the Bach Flower Remedies recommended for shock) for the birth, calendula for if you have to have stitches.

Soft loo paper.

Camera (get a fast film that doesn't need a flash as the sudden light may be a shock for a newborn baby).

Ear plugs.

Lip salve.

Child's rubber ring.

Glucose tablets/honey.

Sanitary towels.

Ice cubes in thermos.

A sponge – but don't make the mistake one man made when asked to pack a sponge (his wife wanted one to cool her face during the labour). He took the floor sponge which was covered in Flash.

The baby!

When we asked if the women we spoke to wished there was anything they hadn't taken, one of them replied, 'Only my husband.'

TIPS

- Make sure your partner's ready – one girl had to wait half an hour after she was ready to go as her husband insisted on changing three times. Well, he said, the NCT lady said it starts out cold and gets hotter later on!

- Make sure *you* are ready; one lady went in wearing her husband's Y-fronts because she couldn't find her own knickers in the rush.

- Ask other mothers to help you make your list to ensure you have everything you need for the birth whether at home or in hospital and also for at home afterwards.

- Turn the waiting weeks just prior to the birth into something positive. Start a course or set yourself a goal so you're not just sitting about counting the minutes.

- Try Egyptian dancing, it is said to have been done in ancient times to help childbirth by loosening up the hips and lower regions.

- Arrange for care after the birth if you can. Find out how long you'll be in hospital. In Kay's case when the nurses asked how long she'd like to stay in, her husband asked if they could arrange for it to be until the end of the football season.

- Get an automatic washing machine.

- Borrow what you can as small babies only poo on new clothes or throw up all over them and they grow out of them so fast. Make sure you have enough to allow for several changes a day – leaks are not uncommon in early days while later puréed carrot is used for finger painting.

- One woman suggested using a shoe horn to stretch the vagina, others suggest vitamin E oil and massage for the perineum to help prevent tearing or the need for an episiotomy (cutting the perineum).

- Organize means of transport for the baby: carry cot for car, carrying sling or buggy for on foot.

- If you're fed up with waiting, sex is rumoured to help labour start as the prostaglandin present in semen helps set the process off. One woman recommends a Bombay curry, then sex. A bonk and a biryani, isn't that how it all started? Other things that have been suggested are: reflexology, acupuncture, jumping up and down, and exercise.

- You'll need support after the birth, try to organize help.

- While you've got time, clear some storage space for the baby. It may mean throwing some things out – not your partner/husband or aged parent though.

- If you can, get a four-door car, much easier for getting loads of stuff in and out off.

- Buy clothes that give you access to the baby. And the baby access to you.

- Buy an answering machine for after the birth so you can answer calls in your own time.

- Make sure other children are well prepared for you to be away for a time, and for the invader.

- Have back-up plans and numbers for transport in case you end up like one lady, who had to drive herself to the hospital with her drunken husband snoring in the back.

- If driving to the hospital, avoid sudden braking.

- Women don't always know when they've gone into labour, could be regular Braxton Hicks contractions which eventually stop hours later, could be indigestion could be IT.

- Don't rely on waters breaking as a sign – *her* waters don't always break . . . his waters sometimes do . . .

(His
Waters
breaking...)

- If the waters do break, try to organize that they do so in Harrods, Mothercare or Marks & Spencer's as they apparently give free layettes or vouchers!

- Call the hospital, or the midwife if it's to be a home birth, if your waters break but still be prepared for the baby to be born four weeks later; do likewise if the contractions start coming at regular intervals of ten minutes or so. If there is bleeding (more than a little pink) call the hospital at once and go in.

- If caught without transport phone for a maternity ambulance.

Memoirs of a mum-to-be

7-9 months

Babies can survive on their own from now on. I found myself wishing mine would want to make an early entrance, but Alexander decided he'd be fashionably late!

I stopped work and was looking forward to putting up my feet and perhaps even doing a bit of needlework or whatever expectant mums did. Was bored out of my mind though.

Steve was travelling again, this time Los Angeles. No chance I could go, so I sought solace in the fridge. I'd already put on more than two stones, and it was obvious I was losing the battle, so what the heck. The hospital was appalled. Eventually, I just made up a weight I thought they'd be happy with! Unfortunately though, my memory wasn't what it used to be and I had forgotten what I told them. During my next visit it seemed that I had lost weight so I had to be wired up to a foetal heart monitor for half an hour . . . never made the same mistake again!

I was bored, so I decided to sell the house, though viewing our new home while I was struggling with contractions wasn't the best way to prepare for the imminent birth.

I was still bored so I went shopping, bought everything the baby could ever need until he was ready to go to university and quite a few things that were completely useless as well. Tell me, what on earth use is a trendy little designer top-and-tail bowl when you've got baby poo running down the arm of your best silk blouse?

I was still bored so I packed, unpacked and repacked my bag for the hospital. In fact I had six bags on standby and still wasn't sure I had everything I needed.

In fact the only things I really needed were a flannel and an understanding partner, but all the rest made me feel prepared. The NCT teacher had told us to take a hot-water bottle – Steve bought me a Tired Tommy Tiger one; I was so embarrassed I didn't dare use it, though it would have been quite handy to ease the backache from contractions.

Apparently some people take a mirror with them to watch the baby's head being born. It's tough enough, without having to witness the imminent arrival of Alien 4! I left mine in my purse.

I was still bored. Fred (the setter, remember) was on constant guard with warm towels and lots of hot water, but Alexander wasn't even contemplating making his exit for weeks yet, so I thought I'd plan a holiday. Did that. Still bored.

Read books about how to tell when labour was imminent. A fascinating chapter in a well-informed American manual advised me that the onset of labour could be predicted by a rush of energy, sudden lethargy, perhaps an urge to eat or loss of appetite, the runs or constipation – should have given birth three months ago by those calculations!

Still bored. Thought I'd oil my perineum! Wheatgerm oil massaged on to the aforesaid area can help prevent the need for an episiotomy, they told me. Didn't work.

Really bored now. Went for even longer walks with Fred, in an attempt to get 'within myself'. That should bring on labour, they said at the yoga class. Didn't work.

I planned an alternative route to the hospital in case any of the roads were blocked. It's only five minutes away, so you can see how bored I was getting.

Then I remembered I hadn't bought a baby bath thermometer. How could my baby survive without a baby bath thermometer during his first few hours of life? I dashed to John Lewis. They didn't have one.

Mothercare – nope, they didn't have one either. I couldn't believe it; I was desperate – didn't these people know just how important it was my baby had his thermometer set up and ready? Thank goodness, they had one in Toys R Us. I could rest easy again.

The yellow duck thermometer safely ensconced in Alexander's bath, I was getting desperately bored now.

Wonder how I can bring on labour? 'Try sex,' suggested friends – you have got to be joking. 'Well, what about a curry, it's supposed to increase your bowel movement and bring on labour.' Crap, said my doctor. I like a man with a sense of humour. My friend Lorraine said she'd spent the last two weeks of her pregnancy jumping up and down stairs all day. Didn't work.

No, the threat of inducing was the thing that worked for me. 'If your baby is not with us by Tuesday we'll have to think about having a little look at your cervix,' said the doctor. No need, thought Alexander, Monday's check-out day. Get my room ready, Mummy, and you be ready too: I'm about to Come On Down.

8 LABOURING IN PAIN

'I had a Jewish delivery. They knock you out with the first pain and wake you up when the hairdresser shows.' *Joan Rivers*

THE MYTH

The birth is going to go according to your plan.

Birth plan A

Dear Doctor:
Totally natural. Come near me with a needle, drug or epidural and you're a dead man.

Birth plan B

Dear Doctor:
Drugs and epidural only as a last resort as I would like to have it as natural as possible. Gas and air I will have, and have some yourself while we're at it.

THE REALITY

Birth plan C

Gimme what you got and some to take home.

The three stages of birth

Birth plan D

Have the baby somehow or other.

Birth plan E

Rip up the birth plan.

Labour can last two hours, it can last 36 and some. This is where your girl guide training comes in handy. You remember the motto. Be prepared . . . for anything.

For partners

What to say when the going gets tough

You're doing really well.

Excellent.

You're strong.

Well done.

Almost there.

What not to say

Yerghh. Dis*gusting*.

I think I'm gonna be sick.

Get a bloody move on.

I can see the head. Crikey, he's ugly. Must take after your side of the family.

Gawd, this is gonna go on all night the way you're going about it.

Fancy a bit of pizza?

Why aren't you breathing the way they showed us in class?

You're looking marvellous . . . (to the nurse)

It's becoming increasingly fashionable these days to play music during the labour and birth. Originally the idea was to have some gentle classical music in the background to help create a tranquil atmosphere for the mother and baby. Not everyone likes the classics, though: one woman timed her contractions to Bette Midler's 'Boogie Woogie Bugle Boys of Company B'. Another woman, determined to give birth to *Madame Butterfly*, had it played over and over. The labour lasted two days; strangely enough, she can't bear to hear that particular piece any more without emitting strange groaning noises.

It takes all sorts, so have the music that inspires you. One woman's Meatloaf is another woman's Orbison . . .

Music not to have

- 'Psychokiller'.
- Carl Orff's *Carmina Burana* (used as theme music to *The Omen*).
- 'Like a Bat out of Hell'.
- 'Stand Up and Fight'.

TIPS

- In the past, symbolism was used to aid births – doors flung open, bottles uncorked, roses flung on water so their petals open, hair loosened, knots untied. If nothing else, it'll give your partner something to do.

- If you need help, take it. There's nothing magical about being in pain. What's magical is the result – the baby.

- Take something to do in early labour. One couple took a radio in – she was later told to quieten her moaning as the contractions came stronger because her husband and gynaecologist couldn't hear the cricket score.

- Take batteries for your radio/TV/video in case there are no spare power points in the birth room. One man got a bit carried away and asked if his wife would unplug the gas-and-air machine so that he could plug in his video.

- If someone is going to be with you during your labour, make sure they check they've got the right room. One eager father-to-be burst into a delivery room in a panic, looked between the legs of the lady straddled there, yelled, 'Oh Christ! That's not Marian' and ran out.

- Upright positions might help, all fours too, squatting, lying, kneeling, standing, sitting. As Janet Balaskas says, think about trying to use a bed pan lying down, then think how much more control you'd have squatting. But whatever works for you. One woman, determined to squat, found when it came to the birth she was most comfortable lying. Another found it awful lying back, then the minute she sat up, she felt better.

- Be prepared to lose control, at least you don't get smacked for it any more (as at the beginning of the century) or have a flannel stuffed in your mouth so you don't disturb the neighbours.

- Take a warm bath, not only for comfort but the warm water is said to speed up the dilation process by twice.

- Some women can't bear to be touched, some find touch and massage very reassuring.

- Make sure your partner is familiar with your birth plan so that if you haven't the energy to insist on something, he knows what you want and can fight for you. Also agree beforehand that if things don't go according to plan you'll give him a signal to say you've really had enough (the V sign, for instance) otherwise he'll be fighting for a natural birth while you know you can't do it any more.

- Don't be afraid to create the atmosphere you want in the birth room. One woman's husband insisted on being naked at the birth as he felt it would help him bond with the new baby. The midwife didn't bat an eyelid, although apparently there was a crowd of nurses outside the delivery room splitting their sides with laughter at the sight of the father-to-be naked except for his face mask and socks.

- Go to the loo often to avoid it coming out over the baby (maybe that's why babies used to be called wee ones).

- Ask the staff to keep you informed as far as they can as to how dilated you are and how much longer you may have to go especially if you are considering pain relief – administered at too late a stage, drugs might affect the baby.

- The gas and air is for the mother, not the father.

- Frédérick Leboyer, the French obstetrician, author of *Birth Without Violence*, urges mothers to be aware of baby's point of view and recommends that the environment the baby comes into be considered since it has just been in a very sheltered, quiet and warm place. He suggests soft lights and quiet, that the baby is not immediately taken away from mother and that the cord is only clamped after it's stopped pulsating.

- Ask doctors to explain what they mean if you don't understand and are worried by something. It might be an innocent comment to them as they've done it before but you are much more vulnerable.

- The most reassuring thing is to have a midwife you know and trust there, she is your everything. But do be aware that shifts can change during hospital births during a long labour. One lady thought she was going insane or had over

dosed on gas and air when the 12-stone Jamaican momma suddenly became a petite Scottish blonde.

- Try not to clockwatch. The three stages – labour, delivery of the baby, and delivery of the placenta – take different lengths of time for different women.

THE MYTH...

We know EXACTLY what we're doing.

THE REALITY...

It's my FIRST delivery...

- Resist the urge to push until the cervix is fully dilated or else it can become puffy and sore. (Normally closed, it opens up during the course of labour up to about 10 centimetres.) The midwife will instruct you.

- Can be sore after the birth, pack a hair dryer for drying yourself (and we don't mean the hair on your head).

★ ★

What advice would you give for during the labour?

- 'Do whatever feels right at the time. There are no rules'
  Helen Lederer
- 'Either natural or needing drugs seem fine to me, unless you can get some synthetic ones'
  Rory McGrath
- 'Don't do it on a bank holiday, at least get a day off work for it'
  Steve Kutner
- 'Have what you need and have no expectations. Don't do a birth plan as you are unlikely to stick to it'
  Mary McGrath
- '*Anything* to stop the pain of contractions . . . Don't be induced unless you are a hundred per cent sure of your dates . . . Breathing shallowly alone ain't enough. If men gave birth there would have been a pain pill a hundred years ago'
  Maureen Lipman

★

Memoirs of a mum-to-be

It's time...

It's true, you do know when it's time, and it's also true that nothing prepares you for the excruciating agony that is laughingly called labour!

At first it was quite exciting really, the gentle contractions were becoming a little more regular and I was looking forward with some anticipation to the birth.

As I mentioned earlier, we went to buy a house while I was contracting. We thought it was quite brave. The owner didn't share our sense of fun and whisked us round so quickly I had whiplash in my neck! I think she was terrified I might gush amniotic fluid all over her best shag pile.

As the twinges became a little stronger I remember thinking that labour was probably not going to be that bad after all, and didn't know what all the fuss about. Later, much later, when I was sure my pelvis was being torn apart by Mr Muscle contestants, I began to appreciate all the warnings I'd been given.

Leading up to that point all was quite straightforward. We'd walked the dogs in the park, had a good night's rest at home and only when my contractions were five minutes apart did we even contemplate contacting the labour ward.

I checked my birth plan, made sure it was all in order (who was I kidding?), repacked my bags again and began loading the car. Steve said we should have employed Pickfords to move us to the hospital. Catching a glimpse of my face he wasn't sure if it was racked with agony or thoughts of murder, so he apologized profusely and said he was sure we'd need every one of the half-dozen cases, and could he get anything else for me?

By the time we reached the hospital I was already three centimetres dilated and well on my way. I was brimming with smug self-confidence and was sure I would be able to cope without even a whiff of gas and air, let alone any type of drug.

As I ambled around the delivery room I remembered tales of blood and gore, so I plumped for a hospital gown rather than wear one of my own nighties. Anyway, they were far too short and at that stage I was still aware of my modesty. Eight hours later, it could have been transparent and wrapped round my ears for all I cared.

Steve brought a tape recorder so we could listen to soothing music as we waited for Alexander to make his appearance. What I didn't know was that it was equipped with a radio as well and that the Arsenal commentary was live on the local station. As the afternoon progressed he did ask if I could pant a little more quietly through my contractions as he might miss a goal. I warned him through gritted teeth that my son would never, never, ever like football!

By mid-afternoon I was still only three centimetres and decided to partake of a little gas and air, which was OK, I conceded, because I had allowed for it on my birth plan.

The midwife thought it best I have my waters broken and even though I had stipulated on my birth plan that I didn't want them broken, after much deliberation we decided that wasn't really medical intervention and agreed. A friend had warned me that her waters had broken in the bath and that it had flooded the room. Didn't believe her, should have done though. Steve was paddling, I was wishing I'd been a better swimmer. It really was gushing everywhere. No turning back now.

An hour later, I was in a muggy, light-headed gas-and-air-induced haze; I remember being quite anxious that supplies might run out, but the midwife assured me provisions were limitless.

By early evening, Steve had sprayed enough water on my face to drain Windermere, we'd abandoned every game of backgammon we'd started, Arsenal had lost miserably, the medical team had changed shifts and I was still only three centimetres.

The NCT and yoga breathing techniques were getting me nowhere, the gas and air wasn't working any more and I decided to go for the big one. I whispered quietly into my loving husband's ear, 'Rip up the birth plan. Clear the decks and bring on the big one – get me an epidural and GET IT NOOWWW.'

9 STAND AND DELIVER

'You wanna know what it's like giving birth? Try sitting on the Eiffel Tower and spinning round.' *Ruby Wax*

THE MYTH

Giving birth is like in the movies – someone shouts for hot water and towels, five minutes later a six-month-old baby is born.

That you'll feel an overwhelming urge to push.

That if you have a Caesarean you won't be able to give birth naturally next time.

That newborn babies look like gorgeous little angels.

You'll feel an immediate overwhelming love for your baby.

THE REALITY

You may not feel like pushing at all, more likely you'll feel an overwhelming urge to go home and call the whole thing off because you've changed your mind and want to go to Katmandu with the milkman.

Far from little cherubs, new babies can look like little purple, grumpy old men with pointy heads and spots. They are also often covered in white stuff called vernix (it keeps the baby's skin from wrinkling in the womb).

Apparently 40 per cent of mothers don't feel an immediate bonding. One friend's memory of 'baby bonding' straight after the birth is that he was handed the newborn at the exact moment his wife started to throw up. He tucked the baby under his right arm, balanced a bucket for his wife in his left hand and that was it, bonding with baby. While the baby's first experience of his mother was of her vomiting violently into a bucket.

If you have to have a Caesarean, your next baby can be delivered naturally. Our friend Jane's was.

Epidurals put a whole new meaning on being legless!

As the first stage of labour gives way to the second, the transition is a time when a lot of women feel that their strength is running out and they've had enough. It is also the last chance for a while to behave *really* badly – so go for it, as after the birth one is supposed to be all giving, self-sacrificing and motherly.

Things that have been said in transition

''S' past my bedtime. I'm going to sleep now.'

'The baby's jammed. We're all dead.'

'I'm losing my mind.'

'Give me DRUGS!'

'Take me to have a Caesarean.'

'OK, that's it. I've had enough. I'm going home now, point me at the car park.'

'That's the last time you ever come near me with that thing.'

Plus various assorted unprintables . . .

How it can feel

Like a large grapefruit pressing against your anus.

All dignity goes out the window as every man and his dog comes and stares at your private bits.

Like shitting an elephant.

Like being hit by Mike Tyson, you get up and he hits you again.

Like a burning-hot cannon with a ball coming out.

Awful not being in control.

'The worst part was the farting; I couldn't help it, it was terribly embarrassing.'

'Well it was tough, but I got over it with a scotch. The hardest part was wheeling her back to her room afterwards' (husband).

★　　　　　　　　　　　　　　　　　　★
What was the best moment during the birth?

- 'Looking at her'
  Helen Lederer
- 'When the epidural went in after sixteen hours' labour without it'
  Maureen Lipman
- 'Learning the child was physically normal'
  Jeffrey Archer
- 'Finally pushing the little sod out!'
  Kay Burley
- 'My wife telling the anaesthetist to bugger off'
  Rory McGrath

- 'Don't know, I was asleep at home'
  Gray Jolliffe

And what was the worst moment for you during the birth?

- 'The anaesthetist actually buggering off without giving *me* anything'
  Rory McGrath
- 'Pain. Pain. They might run out of drugs!'
  Helen Lederer
- 'From the first pain to the moment the epidural went in including the sudden failure of the foetal heartbeat machine'
  Maureen Lipman
- 'The baby kicking me!'
  Jeffrey Archer
- 'Arsenal losing'
  Steve Kutner

What was your partner's role and reaction during the birth?

- 'Always there, stoic, supportive and scared'
  Maureen Lipman
- 'Concern'
  Sue Dawson
- ' "Let me sleep, give me drugs" '
  Rory McGrath
- ' "Don't scream so loud, I can't hear the football results on the radio" '
  Kay Burley

★ ★

TIPS

For the birth

- Rather have a willing friend there than a reluctant partner.
- Some experts advise using creative visualization to help the birth: you shut your eyes and imagine pictures to help the process e.g. breathing as you surf over waves.

- Don't feel guilty if:

  it didn't go the way you'd planned

  you needed more drugs than you'd originally intended

  you are knackered and feel fed up to the back teeth

  you don't feel an immediate bonding with the baby

  you want your partner to suffer as you are

  you have been rude or abusive to the staff during the transition: most of them have got used to it and you can always be nice to them afterwards.

- It's not a competition to see how much you can take. It's more important for babies to be born into an atmosphere where the mothers' OK.

- Don't have expectations about how the baby's going to look.
  'Mary had a little lamb . . . the midwife fainted' *Leonard Rossiter.*

- No such thing as the *right* way; whatever works for you is the right way.

- You can ask for a local anaesthetic if you're having stitches.

• Do whatever works for you.

For partner/friend

• Know when to shut up, you don't want to be a Harry Enfield 'You don't wanna do it like that . . .' type.

• Don't take anything she says too personally, otherwise although *she* recovers nicely from the birth, *you* never will.

What to do with the placenta

In some cultures they bake it in a pie!

Some people eat the placenta as it is supposed to cure post-natal depression and aid stability of hormonal imbalances; sadly in all our research we couldn't find anyone who had actually got round to eating it.

In Northern Borneo the father hangs the placenta in a bamboo container on the porch to announce the birth to the neighbours.

Some people bury it as compost between the dead cat and guinea pig.

Memoirs of a mum-to-be

No turning back now

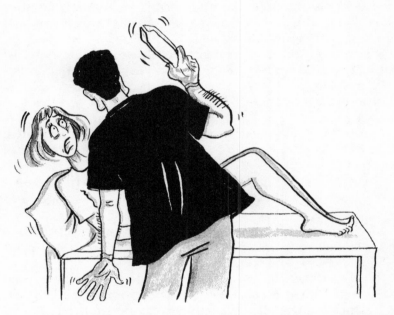

I was knackered, I was in agony and I was faced with the realization which I hadn't accepted before – I was finally going to be a mummy, and it was going to be any time now.

The anaesthetist wandered in and began organizing the epidural. I tried to remain relatively calm as he put a drip in my arm, missed completely and blood, *my blood*, began gushing all over the floor.

'Calm down and it'll be an awful lot better for all of us, dearie,' he said patronizingly. Steve cowered under the delivery table. He knew what was coming.

'It's all right for you, mate,' I screamed in a tone that would have drowned out Concorde. 'Just get *on* with it!'

I think he began to be a little intimidated by this psychopathic madwoman and as he fumbled to put the right needles in the right holes I howled in a stage whisper that would have woken the dead, 'I'm warning you, Steve, get rid of this idiot, he's a complete incompetent.'

My husband tried to suffocate me with a wet flannel while everyone else ignored me and carried on with what they were doing. Of course I was still in control, I was just a little tired and emotional, that's all!

It has to be said that the magnificent, wonderful, soothing, perfectly placed epidural did the trick. Within twenty minutes I'd dilated from three to 10 centimetres, darted through the transition stage without a backward glance and was ready to deliver.

'Push,' they all yelled at me. I felt like I was constipated. 'Come on, push, push, *push*, and he'll be out in a couple of contractions.'

The NCT teacher had said it was like shitting a grapefruit – more like a gigantic watermelon I thought as I struggled to push him out.

'Come on, just another couple of contractions and he's out,' they all yelled. Yeah, yeah, they'd said that last time but I didn't seem to be getting anywhere.

'I can't,' I wailed. 'I just can't do it.' The doctor unpacked his forceps, stood menacingly at the bottom of the bed and as I glanced down I heard him warn 'I can use these, Kay, if you really want me to, but I'm sure you can push this baby out on your own. Which is it to be?'

I couldn't believe it. I was being threatened by a stranger standing between my legs clutching apparatus that resembled torture tackle from the Tower of London.

I had no alternative. Steve gripped my hand, I grabbed the gas and air and all three of us went for it!

Three pushes later and this slimy, mid-blue-coloured alien being slithered in a vernix-covered heap on to my tummy. It was covered in blood and gore and screaming its head off. I looked down in a complete state of shock.

'Congratulations,' said the doctor. 'You have a beautiful baby son.' My first thought was thank God I'd worn a hospital nightie!

Seconds later, it seemed, my legs were in stirrups as the doc patched up the business end. 'Trip out on the gas and air,' he said. 'This won't take long.'

The midwife meanwhile had been cleaning up my newborn and handed over a perfect, sweet-smelling angelic bundle that bore no resemblance to the being that had made his entrance just a few moments before.

I was overcome with emotion. This was my son, my baby, my pride and joy.

'Don't forget to wrap up the placenta,' I said to Steve. 'I want to bury it in the garden under a tree.'

My God I was turning into an earth mother after all. 'Think symbolism' I told him. 'The placenta's what we gave to him.'

Steve replied: 'Put a nappy on top. That's what he gave back.'

10 FROM NOOKIE TO NAPPIES

'People who say they sleep like a baby usually don't have one!' *Leo Burke*

THE MYTHS

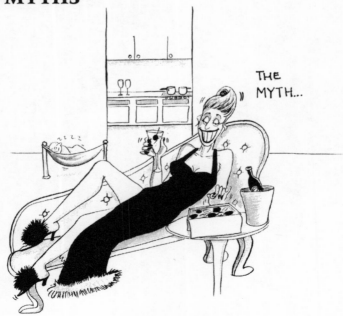

THE MYTH...

A blissful homecoming.

Sympathy, empathy, attention from friends and relatives.

Your figure miraculously snaps back into place.

Happy families.

Babies poo in nappies.

You'll be up and coping in no time as well as looking like someone out of a Doris Day movie.

THE REALITY

Sleepless nights, sore bosoms, the blues. Now's the time you need a three-week holiday with servants, cook and private masseuse.

Babies poo wherever they are. From hard experience, one man told me to warn people of dribbles resembling Weetabix, chicken tikka or what may appear to be a chocolate raisin having lost its packet. If a new baby is in the house, do not, he says in any circumstances put any of this stuff in your mouth.

THE REALITY...

You resent your husband and child for changing you from a sexy showstopper to a tracksuit wearer whose only expression is harassed.

You can look four months' pregnant for six months after the birth.

You can feel an emotional vacuum after birth, an anticlimax – now comes the responsibility.

'The trouble with children is that they're not returnable' *Quentin Crisp.*

You can find yourself resenting the child for your sleepless nights.

None of it's what you expected: 'Oh God, *no*! It's my mother-in-law come back as our Nathaniel!'

The baby gets all the attention. No one wants to hear about your piles, stitches and let-down reflex. You were just the carrier.

You don't know what to do with the baby sometimes. One woman had noticed when she was pregnant that if the baby was kicking whenever she put the food blender on it would always go very still. Thinking this would work after he'd been born, in order to quieten him if he was crying, she tried switching the blender on. He immediately went quiet but by the look on his face, she realized the reaction when he was in the womb hadn't been fascination, but pure terror!

In Malaysia they have the right idea, women are given a massage for twenty days (one a day) after the birth of a child. Over here we trojan on with a stiff upper lip (especially if you had an episiotomy and had to have stitches. . . !).

★   ★

After the birth, what was the best moment for you?

- 'Stroking the incubator'
  Maureen Lipman
- 'Lots – his undiluted love and trust'
  Sue Dawson
- 'Tripping out on gas and air while the doctor perfected his needlepoint on my nether regions'
  Kay Burley
- 'Free drinks at The Roebuck opposite the Royal Free hospital'
  Rory McGrath

After the birth what was the worst moment for you?

- 'Getting thrown out of The Roebuck for singing'
  Rory McGrath
- 'First post-Caesarean pee'
  Maureen Lipman

- 'Father and son already organizing their season ticket allocation for Arsenal'
  Kay Burley
- 'Discovering that the lavatory was wherever baby was sitting'
  Jeffrey Archer
- 'Realizing how fat I was and how hard it was to walk'
  Helen Lederer
- 'Getting woken up at night'
  Gray Jolliffe
- 'Three in the morning, every morning until he was two and a half!'
  Sue Dawson

TIPS

- Not all of your friends will share your enthusiasm, adoration or concern.

- Give yourself time and don't worry if you don't know what to make of him sometimes:
  'We don't know what to make of him.' 'How about a nice rug?' *Nancy Mitford.*

- Post-natal depression (PND) affects 50–75 per cent of mothers, usually a couple of days after the birth; if it lasts longer than a week or two, or is severe, seek help. It is treatable with antidepressants.

- Try to get someone to wait on you hand and foot.

- Beware of sentences that start with 'In our day . . .'

- Don't try to prove you can cope. Ask for help and support.

- Playing a recording of the mother's heartbeat can apparently help send the baby to sleep. (Otherwise: 'If the baby doesn't go to sleep, lay him on the edge of the bed and he will drop off.')

- Don't make fun of your partner's fumbling attempts to help.

- Be aware some older kids don't like now being called big as they may still feel like a baby. Set aside a special time for them.

- Ask visitors not to ignore older children (or you).

- Get a cleaner for the early days even if it's just for a few weeks; save up for it.

- Learn to say no.

- Fix time alone.

- Give yourself time to get back in shape but do keep up post-natal exercises, especially those to strengthen the pelvic floor.

- Learn flattering dress sense (one colour).

- Don't worry too much about your shape. Your partner is probably more concerned that you still have time for him than counting your stretch marks ...

- Have interesting things for the baby to look at. Arrange different places for him to lie for a change of scenery.

- Support the baby's heavy head in the beginning – its neck and backbone are not yet strong enough.

- Don't forget about contraception. Sex may be the last thing on your mind but it'll work its way back in there. You can get pregnant immediately after having a baby. My friend Mary was asked straight after the birth of one of her children what method she was going to use. 'Sex?' she said. 'You've got to be joking, I'm having it all filled in and a gas fire fitted!'

  In the *Guinness Book of Records* the world's most prolific mother is Leotina Albina, who gave birth to her 55th and last child in 1981. The world record is 69 between 1725 and 1765 in Russia: 16 pairs of twins, 7 sets of triplets, 4 sets of quadruplets. So don't forget the condoms!

- Everyone deals with new babies in their own way. As with the whole process, listen to advice, read the books and find what works for you by trial and error.

'When baby's cries grew hard to bear,
I popped him in the Fridgidaire.
I never would have done so if
I'd known that he'd be frozen stiff.
My wife said: George I'm so unhappé!
Our darling's now completely frappé.'

(Harry Graham, 'L'Enfant Glacé',
More Ruthless Rhymes, 1899)

★ ★
What was the reaction of your partner to the birth?

- 'Love at first sight'
Maureen Lipman
- ' "I know you're a partner but I want you off the board" '
Rory McGrath
- 'Very attentive . . . for a few days'
Mary McGrath
- 'Doting'
Jeffrey Archer
- 'Embarrassed'
Sue Dawson
- 'Relief and happiness'
Steve Kutner

★ ★

★　　　　　　　　　　　　　　　　　　★
What was the reaction of friends and family to the new arrival?

- 'A) "I've never seen a baby so like her father" (gynaecologist), B) "She's like a tiny frog – how do you dare to bath her?" (friend)'
  Maureen Lipman
  - 'Glee, joy, delirium, envy, boredom'
  Rory McGrath
- Don't let anyone come and visit you at home, unless they bring food, prearranged flowers and champagne'
  Mary McGrath
- 'Mother pretending not to be ecstatic, sister the same. All surprised I managed it!'
  Helen Lederer
- 'Despair at the football result but hopeful that in a few years' time, the baby will make all the difference on the wing'
  Steve Kutner

★　　　　　　　　　　　　　　　　　　★

Memoirs of a mum-to-be

Going home

This is when the hard work really starts. My child has decided, as in the womb, that it's much more fun being an active rather than a passive newborn, and he loves nothing better than a couple of quick laps round the block in his pushchair – unfortunately it has to be at three o'clock in the morning. God bless Daddy!

At first, I thought Alexander was an angel who slept through the night and only woke for feeds every five to six hours. Didn't know it was the effect of jaundice and wears off round about the time you're starting to think child rearing is easy!

Flowers and friends were arriving in equal numbers. Both needed too much attention, I wailed. Steve took care of it.

The midwife warned that my child had lots of character. When pressed, she said he was a bad-tempered little devil. Ah, his father's temperament. Toddlerdom will be something to look forward to.

11 DRAUGHT OR BOTTLED?

'I don't think my parents liked me. They put a live
teddy bear in my cot.'
Woody Allen

THE MYTH

Breastfeeding comes naturally.

Breastfeeding is one of motherhood's greatest joys.

Babies should be fed every four hours.

Babies should be bathed every day.

THE REALITY

Babies should be fed when they're hungry; this may well be
every four hours at first but like us, they have days when
they are hungrier than others.

A gentle top-and-tail wash will do instead of a bath on some
days.

MYTH

REALITY

Now the baby's born, more loaded decisions have to be made.

The next question is breast or bottle, followed swiftly by the mindbogglingly difficult choice – terries or disposables? There are pros and cons to both arguments. There's no right or wrong, just what's right for you.

THE NEW ~~PARIS~~ *parents'* COLLECTION: That *"Just Splashed"* Look. Topped off with *'Eau de Sick'.*

Dribble marks on their shoulders; she becomes wholesome and starts wearing baggy clothes.

Asleep at dinner.

Wild mad-eyed look.

Books by the bed change: *The Kama Sutra* is replaced by *Breastfeeding and the New Baby.*

They panic when the phone rings every time they go out without the baby. 'Your babysitter's just called. She wants to know where you keep the fire extinguisher.'

The number of EYE BAGS shows the number of days old.

TIPS

- If you can breastfeed do. If you can't – don't worry about it.

- Check out local shops that have facilities for feeding mothers. Give them your business.

- Don't allow yourself to be put off. One lady was told hers were 'not the right kind of nipples'. 'Oh hold on, I'll just nip to the car park and get my others!'

- Buy a shawl for when you need instant privacy from gaping nosies.

- Iced compresses can help engorgement.

- Feed from both sides.

- Avoid certain foods as they can go straight through to the baby – alcohol, spicy food, onions, prunes, for instance, although all babies will react differently.

- If travelling by bus or train, locate your bus ticket before you start feeding the baby so you don't get disturbed.

- If you have to feed in public give appalled onlookers the choice – he screams or feeds.

- Some women say giving water at night is a good idea as most babies'll work out it's not worth waking up for. That is, unless your baby's the incarnation of one of these health writers who advocates we all drink eight glasses of water a day, in which case offer the kid a triple espresso.

- Sit properly with a cushion behind your waist and a pillow on the lap to raise the baby up and your feet on a low foot stool.

And when you've finally got it all together, feeling at peace with all guilt resolved, what do people do? They come in and say:

'So when are you going to give him a brother/sister to play with? Surely you're not going to have an *only* child . . . ?'

Memoirs of a mum-to-be

Draught or bottled?

I'd spent hours reading about breastfeeding before Alexander was born and was led to believe it's the most natural thing in the world.

In fact, it's frustrating, can be embarrassing, and for me the first few weeks were downright agony. I'd been coaxed and cajoled by experts from all sides into believing that it's worthwhile, if only I persevere.

At the moment I can aim no further ahead than one gnawed nipple feed at a time.

On the plus side, it's supposed to help me rediscover my figure much more quickly. That's no problem, I know mine's still there, I just can't find it under all this fat!

Experts and grown-ups tell me to enjoy the first few weeks,

the baby will develop so quickly and we'll never have that special time ever again. As both Alexander and I suffer tears and tantrums, and leak from every orifice, I find it difficult to believe that this is one of the best times in our lives.

Then finally he sleeps, I can shower, remind myself I'm human and Daddy comes home from earning money for the Pampers.

We're a family and it's blooming marvellous. Honestly – you should try it.

★   ★

What advice would you give for coping afterwards?

- 'It will all fall into place when she's six'
  Helen Lederer
- 'There are 3,500,000,000 people on this planet. Each one of them had a mother. Do what they did . . .'
  Gray Jolliffe
- 'It's a learning experience. Nobody trains you for this job – so don't try or expect to be a perfect mother. From day one, admit you know nothing. Sift the advice you are given and be *yourself* – the child will appreciate it. If you attempt to be Mary Earthmother Poppins when you're tired and resentful, they'll sense it and grizzle. Communicate with your baby – talk to her or him. Be their *friend* as they grow, share their curiosity. Learning together is the greatest thrill'
  Maureen Lipman
- 'Read a book in between nappies and nipples – to remind you that you have a brain'
  Mary McGrath

- 'Easy!'
  Steve Kutner
- 'You must be joking!'
  Rory McGrath
- 'Buy some earplugs'
  Kay Burley

★   ★

FINAL TIP

Blessed is she who has no expectation for
she is not disappointed!